Book B

This book belongs to:

....

www.prim-ed.com

My Spelling Workbook *(Book B)*

Published by Prim-Ed Publishing 2011

2nd edition 2011

Reprinted 2015

Copyright© Prim-Ed Publishing 2011

ISBN 978-1-84654-781-2

PR–2281

Titles available in this series:
My Spelling Workbook *(Book A)*
My Spelling Workbook *(Book B)*
My Spelling Workbook *(Book C)*
My Spelling Workbook *(Book D)*
My Spelling Workbook *(Book E)*
My Spelling Workbook *(Book F)*
My Spelling Workbook *(Book G)*

Offices in:

UK and Republic of Ireland:
Marshmeadows
New Ross
County Wexford
www.prim-ed.com

Australia:
PO Box 332
Greenwood
Western Australia 6924
www.ricpublications.com.au

INTRODUCTION

Welcome to *My Spelling Workbook*.

This book and interactive download have lots of activities to help you learn to spell.

You should follow this method when you are learning to spell each word.

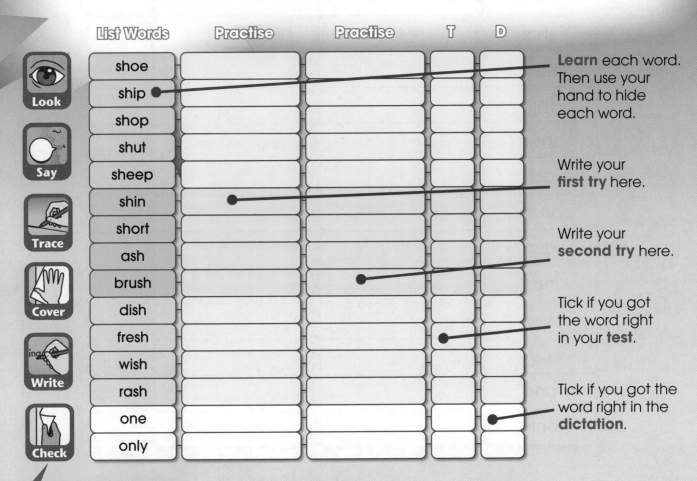

Look

Say

Trace

Cover

Write

Check

List Words	Practise	Practise	T	D
shoe				
ship				
shop				
shut				
sheep				
shin				
short				
ash				
brush				
dish				
fresh				
wish				
rash				
one				
only				

Learn each word. Then use your hand to hide each word.

Write your **first try** here.

Write your **second try** here.

Tick if you got the word right in your **test**.

Tick if you got the word right in the **dictation**.

Contents

Unit 1

sh

Look

Say

Trace

Cover

Write

Check

List Words	Practise	Practise	T	D
shoe				
ship				
shop				
shut				
sheep				
shin				
short				
ash				
brush				
dish				
fresh				
wish				
rash				
one				
only				

What am I?

1. (a) I am long and thin.

    I am below your knee.

    I am part of your leg.

    I am your _____.

    (b) I come in different colours.

    I come in different sizes.

    I am always in a pair.

    I am a _____.

Picture Matching

2. Write the list word that matches each picture.

(a) _____

(b) _____

(c) _____

Crossword

3. Use list words to solve the crossword.

Across

1. You buy things here.
4. Your wear it on your foot.
5. Spots on the skin.
7. There was _____ enough for one.
9. New.
10. To want.
12. A big boat.
13. You eat from one.

Down

2. 5 − 4 = ?
3. A _____ and comb.
4. Not tall.
6. A woolly animal.
8. It's left over after a fire.
11. A bone in the lower part of the leg.
12. Not open.

Word Hunt

4. (a) Which list word is a number? _____

(b) Which list word rhymes with 'pin'? _____

(c) Which list word is the opposite of 'tall'? _____

(d) Write the list word that has 'ee' in it. _____

Letters into Words

5. Write four list words using the letters on the shells.

_____ _____

_____ _____

Unit 1

List Words

shoe
ship
shop
shut
sheep
shin
short
ash
brush
dish
fresh
wish
rash
one
only

Revision Words

can
man
dad
had
the
of

All Mixed Up

6. Unjumble these list words.

(a) srhef _____   (b) epehs _____

(c) hwsi _____   (d) hrsa _____

(e) ohps _____   (f) has _____

Missing Words

7. Complete the sentences using these list and revision words.

only   had   Shut   short

(a) _____ the door behind you.

(b) They _____ a _____ trip
to the park.

(c) I'm _____ going to tell you once
to sit down.

Missing Letters

8. (a) __h__n   (b) sh__ __p

(c) r__s__   (d) s__ __e

Read and Draw

9. (a) A tall ship on the sea.	(b) Dad had red shoes.

sh

Word Search

10. Find the list and revision words in the word search.

shoe	ship	shop
shut	sheep	shin
short	ash	brush
dish	fresh	wish
rash	one	only
can	man	dad
had	the	of

c	a	n	s	h	u	t	c	s
w	i	s	h	b	r	u	s	h
t	v	w	o	n	e	q	h	o
h	s	o	r	a	s	h	i	e
e	h	n	t	e	o	f	p	s
a	i	l	k	t	s	h	o	p
s	n	y	f	r	e	s	h	m
h	v	e	d	i	s	h	a	a
s	h	e	e	p	d	a	d	n

Spelling Sums

11. Find list or revision words.

(a) sh + ort = _____

(b) on + ly = _____

(c) bru + sh = _____

(d) sh + ut = _____

(e) a + sh = _____

(f) m + an = _____

Word Worm

12. Circle each list or revision word you can find in the word worm.

onlydadbrushcanonewishdishshoeof

Memory Master

13. Cover the list words.

(a) Write two from memory. _____ _____

(b) Write a sentence using both words.

_____

_____

_____

Unit ②

Look

Say

Trace

Cover

Write

Check

List Words	Practise	Practise	T	D
chop				
chip				
chin				
chant				
chest				
chum				
such				
torch				
rich				
lunch				
arch				
punch				
church				
two				
three				

Word Hunt

1. (a) Which list words end in 't'?

   _____

   _____

   (b) Which list word rhymes with 'tip'?

   _____

   (c) Write two list words that are numbers.

   _____

   _____

   (d) Write the list word that has 'l' in it.

   _____

Crossword

2. Use list words to solve the crossword.

Across

2. Words said over and over again.
4. The inner side of a foot.
6. It's made from a potato.
7. You can pray here.
11. To hit with your fist.
12. 1 + 1 = ?
13. Not poor.

Down

1. Rhymes with '**much**'.
2. It's under the mouth.
3. 2 + 1 = ?
5. A friend.
7. A treasure _____.
8. To cut.
9. A midday meal.
10. A light you can carry.

Rhyming Words

3. Write list words that rhyme with:

(a) tea _____

(b) munch _____

_____

(c) rip _____

(d) pin _____

Secret Words

4. (a) Take 'c' off 'chip'.

_____

(b) Take 'h' off 'rich' and put in 'e'. _____

(c) Take 'ee' off 'three' and put in 'ow'.

_____

(d) Take 'o' off 'two' and put in 'in'. _____

(e) Take 'ch' off 'chant' and put in 'pl'.

_____

Unit 2

List Words

- chop
- chip
- chin
- chant
- chest
- chum
- such
- torch
- rich
- lunch
- arch
- punch
- church
- two
- three

Revision Words

- set
- wet
- am
- jam
- to
- by

Memory Master

5. Circle the correctly spelled word from the three choices below. Write the word from memory.

(a) three   threa   threy   _____

(b) cest   chest   chess   _____

(c) chuch   church   curch   _____

(d) arch   arech   areh   _____

Missing Words

6. Complete the sentences using these list and revision words.

> jam   torch   wet   chin   set   three

(a) Can you _____ the table?

(b) Use a _____ to find the way.

(c) I like _____ on toast.

(d) My mum had a spot on her _____.

(e) I will be _____ on my next birthday.

(f) My dog was _____ and cold.

Missing Letters

7. Use list or revision words.

(a) ch___ ___ch

(b) ___i___h

(c) l___ ___ch

(d) j___ ___

(e) ___y

(f) c___ ___st

My Spelling Workbook B—Prim-Ed Publishing—www.prim-ed.com

ch

Word Search

8. Find the list and revision words in the word search.

chop	chip	chin
chant	chest	chum
such	torch	rich
punch	lunch	arch
church	two	three
set	wet	am
jam	to	by

b	t	w	o	t	h	r	e	e	s
c	h	o	p	t	o	x	p	w	e
r	e	c	w	c	h	e	s	t	t
i	c	h	i	n	c	g	w	e	t
c	g	u	c	t	c	l	b	a	b
h	s	r	h	g	h	u	y	c	a
x	f	c	i	p	u	n	c	h	r
d	m	h	p	v	m	c	i	a	c
a	m	t	o	r	c	h	m	n	h
j	a	m	s	u	c	h	q	t	e

Picture Matching

9. Look at each picture. Circle the correct word. Write it on the line.

(a)

torch,   torches

_____

(b)

chip,   chips

_____

(c)

churches,   church

_____

Small Words

10. Find small words.

(a) chest _____

(b) torch _____

(c) arch _____

(d) jam _____

(e) chop _____

(f) chin _____

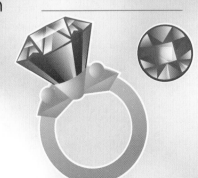

Unit 3

th | **contractions**

Look

Say

Trace

Cover

Write

Check

List Words	Practise	Practise	T	D
than				
them				
then				
those				
these				
both				
tooth				
path				
bath				
I'm				
I'll				
I've				
it's				
four				
five				

Word Worm

1. Circle each list word you can find in the worm.

thanI'veboththesetoothfourthosebath

Word Maker

2. How many words can you make?

_____ _____

_____ _____

_____ _____

pa

ose   too

an   th   en

bo

Crossword

3. Use list words to solve the crossword.

Across

1. 5 − 1 = ?
3. Plural of '**this**'.
5. You use it to bite.
6. A large tub for washing in.
7. Short for '**it is**'.
8. At that time.
9. Two people or things.
10. Short for '**I am**'.

Down

1. 4 + 1 = ?
2. Short for '**I have**'.
3. Plural of '**that**'.
4. A track for walking.
5. Five is one more _____ four.
8. The ones being talked about.
10. Short for '**I shall**' or '**I will**'.

Shape Sorter

4. Write a list word that fits in each shape.

(a)

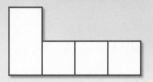

(b)

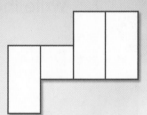

(c)

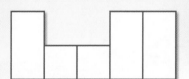

(d)

List Words

than
them
then
those
these
both
tooth
path
bath
I'm
I'll
I've
it's
four
five

Revision Words

win
fin
sip
tip
is
you

Contractions

5. Circle the letters that will be left out to make the contractions. Write the contraction.

(a) I am _____

(b) I have _____

(c) It is _____

(d) I will _____

Missing Words

6. Complete the sentences using these list and revision words.

bath   path   them   I'll   fin   Both

(a) _____ be six on Thursday.

(b) Mum will wash the baby in the _____.

(c) Take the _____ to the left to get to the woods.

(d) _____ of _____ had the same jumper.

(e) A fish has a _____.

Alphabetical Order

7. Write these words in alphabetical order.

path   than   four   bath   you   is

_____

_____

Word Search

8. Find the list and revision words in the word search.

than	them	then
those	these	both
tooth	path	bath
I'm	I'll	I've
it's	four	five
win	fin	sip
tip	is	you

p	a	t	h	a	f	y	o	u
i	f	i	v	e	o	c	t	l
a	i	b	n	l	u	t	h	'v
t	n	a	p	'l	r	h	e	e
o	i	t	's	l	o	e	m	t
o	t	h	o	s	e	n	l	h
t	t	h	e	s	e	z	l	a
h	t	i	p	s	i	p	'm	n
w	i	n	b	o	t	h	i	s

What am I?

9. (a) I am less than six and more than four.

I am _____.

(b) You walk on me and I lead you to places.

I am a _____.

Mixed-up Sentences

10. Unjumble the sentences and write them correctly.

(a) took path. They this

_____

(b) need win. more I four to

_____

(c) bath. Both need a them of

_____

Unit 4

Look

Say

Trace

Cover

Write

Check

List Words	Practise	Practise	T	D
out				
about				
around				
house				
mouse				
now				
down				
how				
brown				
what				
when				
why				
where				
May				
many				

Small Words

1. Find small words.

(a) what _____ _____

(b) when _____ _____

(c) brown _____ _____

(d) many _____ _____

_____ _____

(e) mouse _____ _____

(f) where _____ _____

Spelling Sums

2. Complete the spelling sums.

(a) ar+ou+nd = _____

(b) d+ow+n = _____

(c) wh+y = _____

(d) ou+t = _____

(e) h+ou+se = _____

(f) M+ay = _____

My Spelling Workbook B—Prim-Ed Publishing—www.prim-ed.com

Crossword

3. Use list words to solve the crossword.

Across

1. A month.
3. _____ did you say?
6. On all sides.
10. Opposite of 'in'.
11. At what time?
12. At this time.
13. An animal.
14. Rhymes with 'fly'.

Down

2. Almost.
4. Home.
5. A dark colour.
7. Opposite of 'up'.
8. In what way?
9. In what place?
13. A great number.

Missing Letters

4. Use 'ou', 'ow' or 'wh' to complete the list words.

(a) ___ ___ere   (b) m___ ___se   (c) br___ ___n

(d) ar___ ___nd   (e) h___ ___   (f) ___ ___y

(g) ab___ ___t   (h) ___ ___en   (i) n___ ___

Unit 4

List Words

out
about
around
house
mouse
now
down
how
brown
what
when
why
where
May
many

Revision Words

cot
hot
it
bit
that
if

Word Meanings

5. Match each word to its meaning.

(a) around   •   •   very warm

(b) hot   •   •   month of the year

(c) mouse   •   •   on all sides

(d) May   •   •   a small furry animal

Secret Words

6. Use list or revision words to find the secret words.

(a) Take 'b' off 'brown' and put in 'c'. _____

(b) Add 'sh' to the start of 'out'. _____

(c) Take 'b' off 'bit' and put in 's'. _____

(d) Take 'ar' off 'around' and put in 's'. _____

(e) Take the 'wh' off 'why' and put in 'sh'. _____

Rhyming Words

7. Write list and revision words that rhyme with:

(a) sit _____

(b) day _____

(c) ten _____

(d) cow _____ .

My Spelling Workbook B—Prim-Ed Publishing—www.prim-ed.com

ou ow wh

Word Search

8. Find the list and revision words in the word search.

out	now	when
around	down	why
about	how	where
house	brown	May
mouse	what	many
cot	hot	it
bit	that	if

b	o	u	t	d	o	w	n	w
i	c	a	w	h	a	t	h	h
t	g	r	a	h	o	w	o	e
b	r	o	w	n	l	y	u	n
i	t	u	h	m	o	u	s	e
t	a	n	y	c	o	t	e	n
h	M	d	w	h	e	r	e	o
a	a	b	o	u	t	i	f	w
t	y	m	a	n	y	h	o	t

Memory Master

9. (a) Cover the list words. Write two from memory.

_____   _____

(b) Write a sentence using both words.

_____

Word Hunt

10. (a) Write the revision words that have 'o' in them.

_____   _____

(b) Write the list word that means the same as 'not in'.

_____

(c) Write the list word that is the opposite of 'few'.

_____

(d) Write a revision word that rhymes with 'cliff'.

_____

Look

Say

Trace

Cover

Write

Check

List Words	Practise	Practise	T	D
save				
gave				
take				
make				
came				
made				
like				
ride				
kite				
time				
mime				
crime				
mine				
her				
come				

Rhyming Words

1. Write a list word that rhymes with each of these words.

(a) brave _____

(b) bike _____

(c) hide _____

(d) bite _____

(e) slime _____

(f) spine _____

All Mixed Up

2. Unjumble the list words.

(a) oemc _____

(b) rhe _____

(c) dame _____

(d) atke _____

(e) drei _____

(f) tiek _____

a - e   i - e

Crossword

3. Use list words to solve the crossword.

Across

3. To rescue.
5. Arrived.
7. You do this on a bicycle.
9. A clock tells you this.
10. To build or put together.
11. To enjoy.
13. Opposite of 'go'.

Down

1. Mum has _____ a cake.
2. She always takes _____ time.
4. He _____ me a present.
6. A wrongdoing.
8. Rhymes with 'time'.
9. To hold or grip.
12. You can fly this in the sky.
14. Belonging to me.

Read and Draw

4. (a) I like the kite he gave me.	(b) Mum made some cakes.

Unit 5

List Words

save
gave
take
make
came
made
like
ride
kite
time
mime
crime
mine
her
come

Revision Words

hug
rug
bag
rag
put
was

Mixed-up Sentences

5. Unjumble the sentences and write them correctly.

(a) come It to is home. time

_____

(b) toys. money to like save for I

_____

Word Hunt

6. Use the correct list or revision word.

(a) Which list word starts with 'r'? _____

(b) Which revision words rhyme with '**bug**?'

_____   _____

(c) Which list word means '**to act without words**'?

_____

(d) Which list word is the opposite of '**yours**'?

_____

Spelling Patterns

7. Use the correct colour for these words.

(a) Colour the 'a - e' words red.

(b) Colour the 'i - e' words blue.

gave   crime

like

made   mime

save

a-e i-e

Word Search

8. Find the list and revision words in the word search.

save	made	mime
gave	like	crime
take	ride	mine
make	kite	her
came	time	come
hug	rug	bag
rag	put	was

h	t	c	o	m	e	r	m	a
u	a	g	a	v	e	a	i	m
g	k	z	t	b	a	g	m	a
a	e	m	i	n	e	h	e	d
c	r	i	m	e	j	e	l	e
a	i	s	e	g	z	r	i	p
m	d	a	r	w	a	s	k	u
e	e	v	u	m	a	k	e	t
n	t	e	g	j	k	i	t	e

Missing Letters

9. Write 'a - e' or 'i - e' to complete the list words.

(a) c__m__

(b) g__v__

(c) cr__m__

(d) t__m__

(e) m__d__

(f) l__k__

Fill in the Gaps

10. (a) crime

crim__

cri__ __

cr__ __ __

c__ __ __ __

__ __ __ __ __

(b) mine

min__

mi__ __

m__ __ __

__ __ __ __

(c) take

tak__

ta__ __

t__ __ __

__ __ __ __

	List Words	Practise	Practise	T	D
Look	woke				
Say	home				
	bone				
	note				
Trace	rose				
	cone				
	vote				
Cover	June				
	tune				
Write	use				
	cube				
	tube				
Check	cute				
	seven				
	eight				

Word Worm

1. Circle each list word you can find in the worm.

roseJunesevenhomecubevote

Letters Into Words

2. Write five list words using letters on the apples.

_____ _____

_____ _____

_____

o - e   u - e

Crossword

3. Use list words to solve the crossword.

Across

4. A song.
5. Last night the baby _____ me up.
6. To elect.
9. Paper money.
10. 4 + 3 = ?
14. A dog likes to chew one.
15. A house.

Down

1. Lovable and pretty.
2. You _____ a pencil to write.
3. A flower.
7. A hollow round pipe.
8. You can put ice-cream in one.
11. 10 − 2 = ?
12. The shape of dice.
13. The month before July.

Spelling Rule

Adding 'e' changes the short vowel sound to a long vowel sound.

cut – cute   not – note

4. Use the rule to choose the right word.

(a) The baby looks (cute, cut) _____ in that outfit.

(b) We cook food in a (wok, woke) _____.

(c) A straw is a long (tube, tub) _____.

(d) Dad told (us, use) _____ to play outside.

List Words

woke
home
bone
note
rose
cone
vote
June
tune
use
cube
tube
cute
seven
eight

Revision Words

mix
fox
cut
hut
are
as

Root Words

5. The word '**homes**' is made from the word '**home**'. Circle the letters that have been added and write the root word on the line.

(a) cutting _____

(b) woken _____

(c) cutest _____

(d) votes _____

(e) tuned _____

(f) useful _____

Secret Words

6. Use list or revision words to find the secret words.

(a) Rhymes with '**car.**' _____

(b) Take '**b**' off bone and put in '**st**'. _____

(c) Take '**s**' off '**seven**'. _____

(d) Take '**r**' off rose and put in '**h**'. _____

(e) Add '**een**' to the end of '**eight**'. _____

More Than One

7. Make these words plural by adding '**s**'.

(a) home _____

(b) hut _____

(c) vote _____

(d) rose _____

Word Search

8. Find the list and revision words in the word search.

v	x	t	s	h	o	m	e	c
o	n	u	e	c	u	t	b	u
t	w	n	v	m	i	x	o	b
e	o	e	e	g	c	k	n	e
c	k	i	n	J	u	n	e	r
o	e	g	h	u	t	m	n	o
n	f	h	a	r	e	w	o	s
e	o	t	g	u	s	e	t	e
w	x	a	s	t	u	b	e	n

woke   cone   cube

home   vote   tube

bone   June   cute

note   tune   seven

rose   use   eight

mix   fox   cut

hut   are   as

All Mixed Up

9. Unjumble the list and revision words.

(a) keow _____   (b) xfo _____

(c) veens _____   (d) neut _____

(e) tcu _____   (f) meho _____

Word Meanings

10. Match each word to its meaning.

(a) rose   •   •   hard white part of the body

(b) tune   •   •   flower with thorny stem

(c) bone   •   •   blend

(d) mix   •   •   a pleasing pattern of sound

Unit ⑦

	List Words	Practise	Practise	T	D
Look	sweets				
	king				
Say	Santa				
	carrot				
	happy				
Trace	toys				
	tinsel				
	baby				
Cover	carol				
	sing				
Write	cards				
	food				
Check	gold				
	more				
	any				

Picture Matching

1. Write the word that matches each picture.

(a)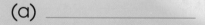

(b)

(c)

What am I?

2. (a) I come from trees.

I am made of paper.

I am sent at Christmas.

I am _____.

(b) I glitter.

I am a metal.

I cost a lot of money.

I am _____.

Christmas

Crossword

3. Use list words to solve the crossword.

Across

2.

3. A popular hymn sung at Christmas.

4.

6. There are _____ boys than girls here.

7.

9. Some.

10. To make musical sounds.

12.

13.

Down

1.

3.

5.

7. Objects for a child to play with.

8. The opposite of 'sad'.

11.

Small Words

4. Find small words.

(a) carrot _____

_____

(b) sweets _____

_____

(c) tinsel _____

_____

_____

(d) gold _____

Word Worm

5. Circle each list word or revision word you can find in the worm.

tinselthangoldkingmoretoys

Unit ⑦

Christmas

List Words

sweets

king

Santa

carrot

happy

toys

tinsel

baby

carol

sing

cards

food

gold

more

any

Word Search

6. Find the words in the Christmas tree word search.

sweets	king
Santa	carrot
happy	toys
tinsel	baby
carol	sing
cards	food
gold	more
any	bells
star	
cake	
tree	
did	
than	

```
                    x
                  d i d
                h a p p y
          a n y f o o d
                  s g t
              t i o o a
            b i n l y c b
          k i n g d s t a r
        d f j s m o r e b i h
          b e l l s t y
        g m l o u r h q y
      s w e e t S c a k e t
    k v s p t c a l n z s w n
  c a r o l e a n t c a r r o t
                r t r
              d a e
              s x e
```

All Mixed Up

7. Unjumble these list and revision words.

(a) roem _____   (b) rete _____

(c) lodg _____   (d) silten _____

(e) slebl _____   (f) tanSa _____

Revision Words

bells

star

cake

tree

did

than

Missing Words

8. Complete the sentences using these words.

happy   carol   star   sing

(a) The shepherds saw a _____ in the sky.

(b) I will be _____ when Christmas comes.

(c) We will _____ a _____ in church.

28   My Spelling Workbook B—Prim-Ed Publishing—www.prim-ed.com

Secret Code

9. Use the secret code to find the message.

a	b	c	h	i	j	n	o	p	s	t	u	v	y
1	2	3	4	5	6	7	8	9	10	11	12	13	14

__ __ __ __ __   __ __   __ __ __ __ __
10 1 7 11 1   5 10   4 1 9 9 14

Spelling Sums

10. (a) ki + ng   = _____ (b) ha + ppy= _____

(c) sw + eets = _____ (d) go + ld   = _____

(e) ca + rds   = _____

Rhyming Words

11. Write a Christmas word that rhymes with these words.

(a) free   _____   (b) treats   _____

(c) nappy   _____   (d) fold   _____

(e) break   _____   (f) parrot   _____

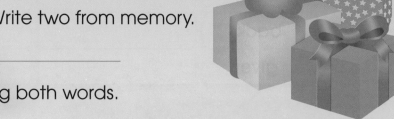

Memory Master

12. (a) Cover the list words. Write two from memory.

_____   _____

(b) Write a sentence using both words.

_____

Read and Draw

13. (a) A star on top of the Christmas tree.

(b) A happy king eating cake.

Unit 8

dr gr tr br cr

Look

Say

Trace

Cover

Write

Check

List Words	Practise	Practise	T	D
drum				
drip				
drop				
grip				
grab				
grim				
trip				
try				
trim				
bring				
brave				
crab				
crash				
back				
give				

Word Hunt

1. (a) Which list words end in 'ip'?

_____ _____ _____

(b) Which list words have five letters?

_____ _____ _____

(c) Which list word rhymes with 'sack'? _____

(d) Which list word ends in 'ing'? _____

Spelling Sums

2. (a) br + ing = _____   (b) tr + im = _____

(c) dr + op = _____   (d) gi + ve = _____

(e) gr + ab = _____   (f) cr + ash = _____

dr **gr** **tr** **br** **cr**

Crossword

3. Use list words to solve the crossword.

Across

1. Opposite of 'front'.
3. Very serious.
5. Showing courage.
7. Make an effort to do something.
9. To hold or grasp.
11. To let fall.
13. To cut something and make neat.
14. To snatch.

Down

2. We found a _____ on the beach.
3. To hand over.
4. A car accident.
6. To fall in small amounts.
8. To stumble or fall.
10. A musical instrument.
12. To fetch or carry.

Read and Draw

4. (a) A crab can grip with its claws.

(b) A drum goes crash and bang.

Unit 8

dr | gr | tr | br | cr

List Words

drum
drip
drop
grip
grab
grim
trip
try
trim
bring
brave
crab
crash
back
give

Revision Words

we
me
be
bed
with
his

Rhyming Words

5. Choose a rhyming word from the list and revision words.

(a) fed _____

(b) sip _____

(c) track _____

(d) sing _____

(e) fly _____

(f) slim _____

Word Meanings

6. Match each word to its meaning.

(a) grim •   • fetch

(b) trip •   • very serious

(c) grip •   • a sea animal

(d) bring •   • take a tight hold

(e) crab •   • a journey

Alphabetical Order

7. Write these words in alphabetical order.

trim   grab   we   crash   his   bring

_____

_____

_____

_____

_____

_____

Word Search

8. Find the list and revision words in the word search.

drum	grim	brave
drip	trip	crab
drop	try	crash
grip	trim	back
grab	bring	give
we	me	be
bed	with	his

g	r	i	p	b	e	b	e	d
g	c	t	r	i	m	g	b	g
b	r	g	i	v	e	r	r	r
a	a	z	t	r	y	a	a	i
c	b	r	i	n	g	b	v	m
k	w	t	d	r	i	p	e	h
z	i	r	c	r	a	s	h	i
w	t	i	m	d	r	o	p	s
e	h	p	e	p	d	r	u	m

Missing Letters

9. Use list or revision words.

(a) __ru__ (b) cra__ __ (c) wi__ __

(d) __i__ (e) b__a__e (f) __r__ __g

Memory Master

10. (a) Cover the list words. Write two from memory.

_____ _____

(b) Write a sentence for each word.

_____

_____

_____

_____

Unit 9

st

Look

Say

Trace

Cover

Write

Check

List Words	Practise	Practise	T	D
stamp				
stop				
stand				
step				
start				
stone				
stem				
nest				
rest				
best				
cost				
must				
lost				
nine				
help				

Small Words

1. Find small words.

(a) must _____

(b) nine _____

(c) help _____

(d) best _____

(e) stop _____

Word Maker

2. How many words can you make?

_____

_____

_____

_____

_____

_____

_____

amp

co   ne

st

em   be

mu   one

My Spelling Workbook B—Prim-Ed Publishing—www.prim-ed.com

Crossword

3. Use list words to solve the crossword.

Across

2. Main part supporting a flower.
7. To end.
8. Price.
10. A bird's home.
12. The finest, the highest.
13. One less than ten.
14. You stick it on an envelope.
15. Time off.

Down

1. Move one leg in front of the other.
3. Have to do something.
4. A pebble.
5. Not found.
6. Opposite of 'sit'.
9. To lend a hand.
11. To begin.

Correct Words

4. Write the correct word.

(a) Can you [stand/stood] _____ still?

(b) He [stand/stood] _____ for an hour

and a half watching the match.

(c) I hope I do not [lose/lost] _____ my way!

(d) I have [lose/lost] _____ my way!

List Words

stamp
stop
stand
step
start
stone
stem
nest
rest
best
cost
must
lost
nine
help

Spelling Rule

Look how the 'ed' is added to these words.

jump → jumped   (Only 'ed' is added.)

rip → ripped   (The last letter is doubled to keep the vowel sound short.)

5.   Add 'ed' to the words below.

(a) Only 'ed' is added.

rest   _____

stamp   _____

(b) Last letter is doubled before 'ed' is added.

stop   _____   step   _____

Secret Words

6.   Use list or revision words to find the secret words.

(a) Rhymes with 'mow'.   _____

(b) Take 'st' off 'stand' and put in 'b'.   _____

(c) Take 'y' off 'they'.   _____

(d) Take 'c' off 'cost' and put in 'p'.   _____

(e) Add 'ful' to the end of 'help'.   _____

More Than One

7.   Make these words plural by adding 's'.

(a) step   _____

(b) leg   _____

(c) nest   _____

(d) stone   _____

Revision Words

leg
beg
ten
men
they
no

My Spelling Workbook B—Prim-Ed Publishing—www.prim-ed.com

Word Search

8. Find the list and revision words in the word search.

stamp	stone	cost
stop	stem	must
stand	nest	lost
step	rest	nine
start	best	help
leg	beg	ten
men	they	no

s	t	a	n	d	v	s	s	m
n	o	r	e	s	t	t	t	e
h	e	l	p	t	h	o	o	n
l	e	g	l	a	e	n	p	i
t	e	n	o	r	y	e	s	n
s	m	u	s	t	c	m	t	e
b	e	s	t	c	o	u	e	h
b	e	g	n	e	s	t	p	e
s	t	e	m	s	t	a	m	p

What am I?

9. (a) I come in different sizes.

I can be found in a garden.

I am hard.

I am a _____.

(b) I am a home.

I am soft and warm.

I was made by an animal or bird.

I am a _____.

Mixed Up Sentences

10. Unjumble the sentences and write them correctly.

(a) must starting hill. stop rest You before up the and

_____

(b) stamps? much ten it How cost for does

_____

Unit 10

Look

Say

Trace

Cover

Write

Check

List Words	Practise	Practise	T	D
skip				
skin				
skid				
skirt				
spell				
spit				
spin				
spot				
spark				
swim				
swing				
sweep				
swell				
good				
who				

Shape Sorter

1. Write a list word that fits in each shape.

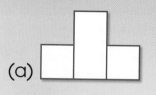
(a)

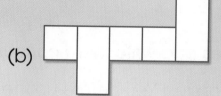
(b)

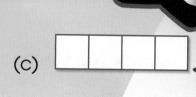
(c)

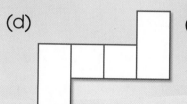
(d)

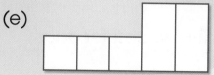
(e)

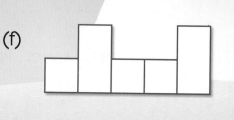
(f)

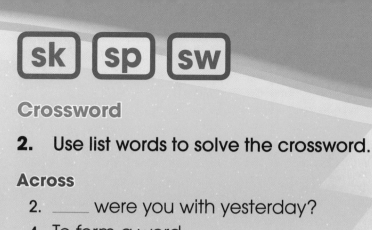

| sk | sp | sw |

Crossword

2. Use list words to solve the crossword.

Across

2. _____ were you with yesterday?
4. To form a word.
5. It covers your body.
6. To clean by brushing.
7. To slide.
8. Girls' clothing.
9. To move through water.
10. Opposite of '**bad**'.

Down

1. To become larger.
3. Turn round quickly.
5. A hot _____ shot out of the fire.
6. Jump lightly off the ground.
7. To force liquid from the mouth.
8. To move from side to side.
9. A small round mark.

Spelling Rule

Look how the '**ing**' is added to these words.

jump → jumping   (Only '**ing**' is added.)

run → running   (The last letter is doubled to keep the vowel sound short.)

3. Add '**ing**' to the words below.

(a) Only '**ing**' is added.

sweep _____   spell _____   swing _____

(b) Double last letter and add '**ing**'.

spin _____   skip _____   swim _____

Unit 10

sk | sp | sw

List Words

- skip
- skin
- skid
- skirt
- spell
- spit
- spin
- spot
- spark
- swim
- swing
- sweep
- swell
- good
- who

Revision Words

- my
- by
- mop
- top
- for
- on

All Mixed Up

4. Unjumble the words.

(a) kids _____   (b) tips _____

(c) gsnwi _____   (d) nips _____

(e) karps _____

Picture Matching

5. Write a list or revision word that matches each picture.

(a)

_____

(b)

_____

(c)

_____

(d)

_____

Rhyming Words

6. Write list or revision words that rhyme with:

(a) fly _____   _____

(b) bell _____   _____

(c) thin _____   _____

(d) hop _____   _____

More Than One

7. Make these words plural by adding 's'.

(a) spark _____

(b) spot _____

(c) mop _____

(d) skirt _____

My Spelling Workbook B—Prim-Ed Publishing—www.prim-ed.com

Word Search

8. Find the list and revision words in the word search.

skip	spit	swing
skin	spin	sweep
skid	spot	swell
skirt	spark	good
spell	swim	who
my	by	mop
top	for	on

b	s	k	i	d	k	s	s	w
s	p	i	n	o	n	w	p	h
a	a	t	o	p	s	e	i	o
j	r	s	k	i	p	e	t	s
s	k	i	n	f	o	p	g	k
w	b	y	t	o	t	s	o	i
e	n	m	y	r	b	w	o	r
l	s	w	i	n	g	i	d	t
l	s	p	e	l	l	m	o	p

Synonyms

9. Find a list word with a similar meaning.

(a) flash _____   (b) expand _____

(c) twirl _____   (d) slip _____

Missing Words

10. Complete the sentences using these list and revision words.

for	Who	skin	swell

(a) Pasta will _____ when you cook it.

(b) Dad has to buy petrol _____ the car.

(c) My _____ felt so cold after the shower of rain.

(d) _____ knows the way to Dublin?

Unit 11

ent · ant · amp · ump

List Words	Practise	Practise	T	D
went				
spent				
rent				
ant				
pant				
grant				
damp				
lamp				
ramp				
camp				
jump				
bump				
lump				
some				
has				

 Look
 Say
 Trace
 Cover
 Write
 Check

Word Worm

1. Circle each word you can find in the worm.

Letters Into Words

2. Write six list words using letters on the branch.

_____ _____

_____ _____

_____ _____

haswentantsomelumpgrant

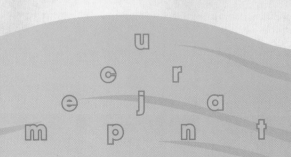

Crossword

3. Use list words to solve the crossword.

Across

2. I have one and she ___ one.
4. Yesterday, I ___ shopping.
5. 'I ___ you three wishes', said the fairy.
8. We will ___ in that field.
10. I have ___ all my pocket money.
11. A chunk.
13. To hit or strike.

Down

1. It was so hot the dog began to ___.
3. Money paid for the use of a house.
6. Beside the stairs there is a ___ for wheelchairs.
7. Slightly wet.
9. A small insect.
10. An unknown amount.
11. A light.
12. To leap.

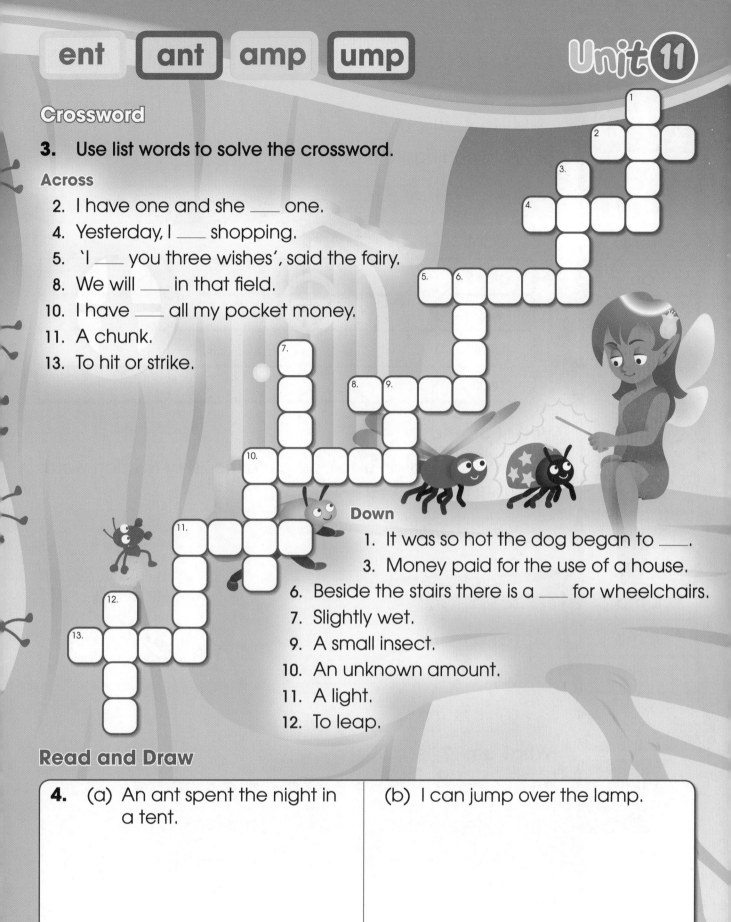

Read and Draw

4. (a) An ant spent the night in a tent.

(b) I can jump over the lamp.

List Words

went

spent

rent

ant

pant

grant

damp

lamp

ramp

camp

jump

bump

lump

some

has

Revision Words

see

been

meet

need

yes

saw

Adding Endings

5. Add endings to make new words.

	Add 's'	Add 'ed'	Add 'ing'
pant			
grant			
need			
jump			
rent			

Vowel Sounds

6. Use 'a', 'e', 'o' or 'u' to complete the list or revision words. Write the word.

(a) s__me _____

(b) s__w _____

(c) b__mp _____

(d) sp__nt _____

(e) h__s _____

(f) c__mp _____

What am I?

7. (a) I am a tool.

I have teeth.

I cut things.

I am a _____.

(b) You turn me on and off.

I have a plug.

I give off light.

I am a _____.

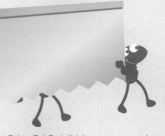

ent ant amp ump

Word Search

8. Find the list and revision words in the word search.

went	grant	jump
spent	damp	bump
rent	lamp	lump
ant	ramp	some
pant	camp	has
see	been	meet
need	yes	saw

s	p	e	n	t	c	a	m	p
o	b	s	r	l	y	e	s	a
m	e	e	t	u	m	r	t	n
e	e	e	u	m	w	e	n	t
a	n	t	s	p	d	n	e	a
g	r	a	n	t	a	t	e	j
h	i	s	l	a	m	p	d	u
a	e	r	a	m	p	b	e	m
s	a	w	o	n	b	u	m	p

Memory Master

9. Circle the correctly spelled word from the three choices below. Write the word from memory.

(a) some   sume   soam   _____

(b) maet   mete   meet   _____

(c) bumb   bump   dunb   _____

Word Meanings

10. Match each word to its meaning.

(a) ramp   •   •   money for use of a house

(b) damp   •   •   an urgent want

(c) rent   •   •   slope joining two levels

(d) need   •   •   a bit wet

Unit 12

ea ee

	List Words	Practise	Practise	T	D
Look	meat				
Say	teach				
	reach				
	beat				
	seat				
Trace	dear				
	hear				
Cover	fear				
	heat				
Write	steep				
	keep				
	sleep				
Check	sheet				
	would				
	pupil				

Missing Letters

1. Write 'ee' or 'ea' in the following words.

   (a) sl___ ___p

   (b) h___ ___r

   (c) t___ ___ch

   (d) s___ ___t

   (e) k___ ___p

   (f) r___ ___ch

Small Words

2. Find small words.

   (a) meat _____

   _____ _____

   (b) sheet _____ _____

   (c) hear _____ _____

   (d) seat _____

   _____ _____

   (e) teach _____ _____

46   My Spelling Workbook B—Prim-Ed Publishing—www.prim-ed.com

ea ee

Crossword

3. Use list words to solve the crossword.

Across

3. A butcher's shop sells _____.
4. School child.
5. The letter started, '_____ Jane'.
7. You write on a _____ of paper.
9. I could feel my heart _____.
11. Fright or panic.
13. Nap.
14. Warmth.

Down

1. I rolled down a _____ hill.
2. Rhymes with 'could'.
6. Arrive.
7. Chair.
8. To listen to.
10. To hang on to.
12. To give lessons.

Proofreading

4. Circle the list word that is spelt incorrectly. Write it correctly in the box.

(a) I can't heer you.

(b) Make sure that the meet is well cooked.

(c) Can you teech me how to drive?

(d) Write a note on that sheat of paper.

(e) Wood you like to come to the park?

Unit 12

ea | ee

List Words

meat
teach
reach
beat
seat
dear
hear
fear
heat
steep
keep
sleep
sheet
would
pupil

Revision Words

moon
room
all
call
this
have

Word Hunt

5. (a) Which list words rhyme with '**clear**'?

_____ _____ _____

(b) Which list words rhyme with '**beach**'?

_____ _____

(c) Which word means the '**opening in the centre of your eye**'? _____

(d) Which word is the opposite of '**give away**'? _____

All Mixed Up

6. Unjumble these list and revision words.

(a) tepes _____

(b) lacl _____

(c) careh _____

(d) ldwuo _____

(e) stih _____

Alphabetical Order

7. Write these list and revision words in alphabetical order.

room   beat   all
steep   fear   keep

_____

_____

_____

_____

_____

_____

My Spelling Workbook B—Prim-Ed Publishing—www.prim-ed.com

Word Search

8. Find the list and revision words in the word search.

meat	dear	keep
teach	hear	sleep
reach	fear	sheet
beat	heat	would
seat	steep	pupil
moon	room	all
call	this	have

s	h	e	e	t	m	o	o	n
t	a	o	k	e	e	p	s	w
e	v	z	r	e	a	c	h	o
e	e	s	e	a	t	a	e	u
p	u	p	i	l	r	l	a	l
t	e	a	c	h	a	l	t	d
h	e	a	r	o	o	m	x	e
i	b	e	a	t	a	l	l	a
s	l	e	e	p	f	e	a	r

Missing Words

9. Complete the sentences using these list and revision words.

moon   seat   beat   pupil

(a) The _____ on the bus was broken.

(b) There was a full _____ last night.

(c) Can you _____ that high score?

(d) There is a _____ in my class who is blind.

Spelling Patterns

10. Use the correct colour for these words.

(a) Colour the 'ea' words red.

(b) Colour the 'ee' words blue.

(c) Colour the other words green.

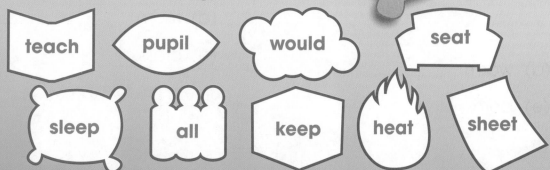

teach   pupil   would   seat   sleep   all   keep   heat   sheet

Unit 13

Spring/Easter

	List Words	Practise	Practise	T	D
Look	hunt				
Say	eggs				
	born				
	thorn				
Trace	bunny				
	basket				
	flower				
Cover	park				
	plant				
Write	cross				
	raindrop				
	spring				
Check	warm				
	thirteen				
	Monday				

Small Words

1. Find small words.

(a) Monday _____ _____

(b) plant _____ _____

_____

(c) basket _____ _____

_____

(d) warm _____ _____

(e) born _____

More Than One

2. Make these words plural by adding '**s**' or '**es**'.

(a) raindrop _____

(b) basket _____

(c) flower _____

(d) thorn _____

(e) cross _____

Spring/Easter

Crossword

3. Use list words to solve the crossword.

Across

2. The day after Sunday.

3. The baby was _____ on Monday.

4. 6. To chase animals for food.

7. Fairly hot.

9. Jesus was nailed to a _____.

11.  13.

14.

Down

1. A large public garden in a town.

3.

5. Comes after 12.

8.

10. The season before summer.

12. A sharp point growing on plants or trees.

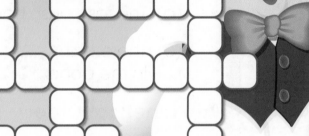

Letters Into Words

4. Write five list words using letters on the eggs.

_____

_____

_____

_____

_____

Word Worm

5. Circle each list word you can find in the word worm.

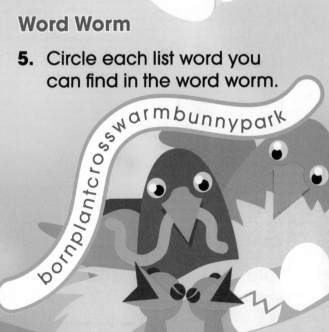

bornplantcrosswarmbunnypark

Spring/Easter

List Words

- hunt
- eggs
- born
- thorn
- bunny
- basket
- flower
- park
- plant
- cross
- raindrop
- spring
- warm
- thirteen
- Monday

Word Meanings

6. Match each word to its meaning.

(a) plant •   • angry

(b) basket •   • grows in soil or water

(c) cross •   • child's word for a rabbit

(d) bunny •   • container made of thin strips of cane

Missing Words

7. Complete the sentences using these words.

thorns   thirteen   eggs   hunt   frogs

(a) Let's _____ for our Easter _____.

(b) The rose bush had lots of sharp _____.

(c) There are _____ _____ in the pond.

Alphabetical Order

8. Write these words in alphabetical order.

here   raindrop   frog   thirteen   dig

_____

Read and Draw

9. (a) A bunny in the park in the rain.	(b) A basket of flowers with thorns.

Revision Words

- bee
- bud
- dig
- frog
- ask
- here

Spring/Easter

Word Search

10. Find these words in the Easter egg word search.

hunt	eggs	born
thorn	bunny	basket
flower	park	plant
cross	raindrop	spring
warm	thirteen	Monday
bee	bud	dig
frog	ask	here

```
        y a b t s
      i r k x a p n
      y l t h o r n d z
    s r a i n d r o p p c
    i b o r n w p l a n t
    e g g s b u n n y M t
    i s f l o w e r v o h
    f p b h u n t l h n i
    r r g t r o r n f d r
    o i j g p a r k s a t
    g n c r o s s n a y e
    d g b b a s k e t p e
    e r e t h e r e s j n
    g v a w a r m n d i g
      h t a s k d n p o
      v b e e s p k
        w b u d t
```

Rhyming Words

11. Write a spring or Easter word that rhymes with these words.

(a) sunny _____

(b) bark _____

(c) loss _____

(d) bring _____

(e) hour _____

(f) pegs _____

Secret Words

12. (a) Take 'cr' off 'cross' and put in 'fl'. _____

(b) Take 't' off 'plant' and put in 'e'. _____

(c) Take 'b' off 'born' and put in 'c'. _____

(d) Take 'w' off 'warm' and put in 'h'. _____

Unit 14

Look

Say

Trace

Cover

Write

Check

List Words	Practise	Practise	T	D
bang				
hang				
sang				
song				
along				
belong				
wing				
king				
ring				
thing				
being				
hung				
sung				
old				
their				

Word Worm

1. Circle each word you can find in the word worm.

sungbeingbelongoldwinghung

Letters Into Words

2. Write six list words using letters in the gold bars.

_____

_____

_____

_____

_____

_____

o   n
d   g
b   k
a   l
i   s

ang ong ing ung

Crossword

3. Use list words to solve the crossword.

Across

3. The kite _____ from a tree.
5. I can wear a _____.
6. Sudden, loud noise.
8. Belonging to them.
10. To be owned by someone.
12. He walked _____ the path.
14. _____ the picture on the wall.

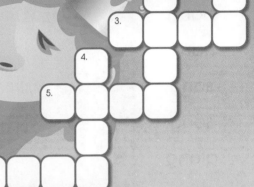

Down

1. A bird needs it to fly.
2. The song being _____ was too loud.
4. A male ruler.
6. You are _____ silly.
7. Any object.
9. Sing a _____.
11. He _____ a song.
13. Opposite of young.

Compound Words

A compound word is made by joining two words.

For example, **ring** + **side** = ringside

4. (a) Circle the words you can join to '**thing**' to make a new word.

(b) Write the words.

yes	any
some	**thing**	all
sun	every

_____

_____

_____

List Words

bang
hang
sang
song
along
belong
wing
king
ring
thing
being
hung
sung
old
their

Memory Master

5. Cover the list words.

(a) Write two from memory.

_____ _____

(b) Write a sentence using both words.

_____

_____

_____

Secret Words

6. (a) Rhymes with '**gold**'. _____

(b) Take '**s**' off '**sand**' and put in '**st**'. _____

(c) Take '**ing**' off '**being**' and put in '**side**'.

_____

(d) Take '**h**' off '**hung**' and put in '**r**'. _____

(e) Take '**l**' off '**long**' and put in '**str**'. _____

Read and Draw

7. (a) He sang the song well. | (b) The king had a large ring.

Revision Words

and
sand
lend
end
from
want

Word Search

8. Find the list and revision words in the word search.

t	s	o	n	g	w	a	n	t
h	a	n	d	o	i	r	b	h
e	n	d	s	l	n	a	e	i
i	d	k	t	d	g	l	l	n
r	s	i	b	e	l	o	n	g
h	u	n	g	b	a	n	g	h
e	n	g	r	i	n	g	u	a
o	g	a	f	r	o	m	p	n
l	e	n	d	i	s	a	n	g

bang belong being

hang wing hung

sang king sung

song ring old

along thing their

and sand lend

end from want

Make New Words

9. Add '**ing**'.

(a) bang → She was _____ on the door.

(b) lend → Megan did not like _____ me the book.

(c) ring → Kevin kept _____ the doorbell.

Shape Sorter

10. Write a list or revision word that fits in each shape.

(a)

(b)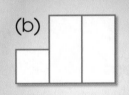

(c)

(d)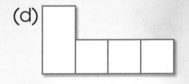

(e)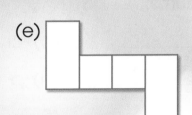

(f)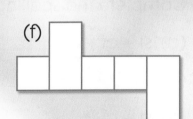

Unit 15   ay   ai

Look

Say

Trace

Cover

Write

Check

List Words	Practise	Practise	T	D
away				
day				
stay				
clay				
pay				
ray				
mail				
stain				
pain				
sail				
tail				
wait				
train				
Tuesday				
Wednesday				

Memory Master

1. Circle the correctly spelled word from the three choices below.
Write the word from memory.

(a) trayn   train   trean   _____

(b) away   avay   awai   _____

(c) Wedesday   Wednesday   Wedneday   _____

Spelling Sums

2. Complete the spelling sums.

(a) st + ai + n = _____   (b) cl + ay = _____

(c) m + ai + l = _____   (d) p + ai + n = _____

(e) st + ay = _____   (f) w + ai + t = _____

Crossword

3. Use list words to solve the crossword.

Across

2. Letters sent by post.
3. Go ____!
8. 24 hours in a ____.
9. It runs on a railway track.
11. A dirty mark.
12. The day after Monday.
14. Money given for work.

Down

1. Used for making bricks.
4. I had to ____ a long time for a bus.
5. Day before Thursday.
6. Beam of light.
7. An ache.
10. A ship set ____.
13. Remain.

Make New Words

4. Add 'ed' to these words and complete the sentences. One word is irregular. Can you find it?

(a) wait → She _____ for the bus at the bus stop.

(b) sail → The large ship _____ across the bay.

(c) stay → I _____ indoors as it was raining yesterday.

(d) pay → The man _____ for his milk and left the shop.

Unit 15

List Words

away
day
stay
clay
pay
ray
mail
stain
pain
sail
tail
wait
train
Tuesday
Wednesday

Revision Words

hop
pop
fly
sky
pen
den

Word Meanings

5. Match each word to its meaning.

(a) den •   • letters sent or delivered by post

(b) ray •   • a mark that is difficult to take away

(c) mail •   • home of a wild animal

(d) stain •   • a line of light or heat

Word Maker

6. How many list words can you make?

s
st
m   n
p   ai   l
t   t
w

_____
_____
_____
_____
_____

More Than One

7. Make these words plural by adding '**s**' or '**es**'. One is made plural by dropping the '**y**' and adding '**ies**'.

(a) day _____

(b) tail _____

(c) fly _____

(d) ray _____

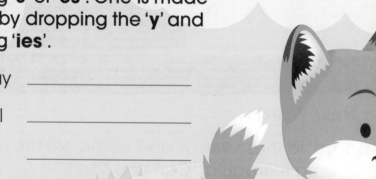

ay | ai

Word Search

8. Find the list and revision words in the word search.

away	ray	tail
day	mail	wait
stay	stain	train
clay	pain	Tuesday
pay	sail	Wednesday
hop	pop	fly
sky	pen	den

W	a	i	t	a	s	k	y	m
e	p	o	p	i	t	p	t	a
d	e	n	c	t	a	a	r	i
n	n	s	l	a	i	y	a	l
e	t	r	a	i	n	u	y	e
s	t	a	y	l	f	l	y	p
d	a	y	h	o	p	o	r	a
a	w	a	y	s	a	i	l	i
y	T	u	e	s	d	a	y	n

All Mixed Up

9. Unjumble these list and revision words.

(a) napi   _____

(b) irant   _____

(c) saydueT   _____

(d) yks   _____

(e) yalc   _____

(f) npe   _____

Missing Words

10. Complete the sentences using these list or revision words.

pain   clay   den   Wednesday

(a) The day after Tuesday is _____.

(b) I felt a _____ in my leg.

(c) The little fox cub crawled out of his _____.

(d) We made _____ pots in our art lesson.

Unit 16

 Look

 Say

 Trace

Cover

Write

Check

List Words	Practise	Practise	T	D
bird				
girl				
first				
third				
twirl				
hurt				
turn				
burn				
surf				
paper				
never				
over				
under				
Friday				
Thursday				

Word Hunt

1. (a) Which word is the opposite of 'last'? _____

   (b) Which word is the opposite of 'always'? _____

   (c) Which word has the most letters? _____

   (d) Which word has the name of an animal in the middle of it?

   _____

   (e) Which word means 'spin'? _____

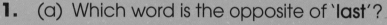

Crossword

2. Use list words to solve the crossword.

Across

1. A robin, a crow or a lark.
2. First, second and ____.
3. One before second.
6. Day before Saturday.
7. To spin or turn.
8. You write on it.
10. Not ever.
12. Below.

Down

1. To be on fire.
2. Day before Friday.
4. Foam formed by waves breaking.
5. Opposite of 'boy'.
7. To move round.
9. Opposite of 'under'.
11. To cause pain.

Spelling Patterns

3. Use the correct colour for these words.

(a) Colour the '**er**' words red.

(b) Colour the '**ir**' words yellow.

(c) Colour the '**ur**' words green.

(d) Colour all other words blue.

Friday	never
twirl	third
burn	cover
surf	Thursday

Unit 16

ir **ur** **er**

List Words

- bird
- girl
- first
- third
- twirl
- hurt
- turn
- burn
- surf
- paper
- never
- over
- under
- Friday
- Thursday

Revision Words

- hood
- zoo
- feed
- seen
- weed
- seed

Mixed-up Sentences

4. Unjumble the sentences and write them correctly.

(a) had bird so life. much seen The never seed its in

_____

_____

(b) the over You bridge under go the must hill and zoo. the to get to

_____

_____

_____

Correct Words

5. Write the correct word.

(a) Ten | grils/girls | _____ came to my party.

(b) I have | seen/saw | _____ that film before.

(c) We will go to the park on | Thurday/Thursday | .

_____.

(d) Can you | fed/feed | _____ the dog, please?

Secret Words

6. (a) Take 'un' off 'under' and put in 'won'. _____

(b) Add 'm' to the end of 'zoo'. _____

(c) Take 'd' off 'third' and add 'teen'. _____

(d) Take 'h' off 'hood' and add 'st'. _____

All Mixed Up

7. Unjumble these list and revision words.

(a) furs _____ (b) nese _____

(c) trisf _____ (d) roev _____

(e) rutn _____ (f) ozo _____

ir ur er

Word Search

8. Find the list and revision words in the word search.

bird	hurt	never
girl	turn	over
first	burn	under
third	surf	Friday
twirl	paper	Thursday
hood	zoo	feed
seen	weed	seed

t	h	i	r	d	e	h	u	r	T
w	o	n	p	a	p	e	r	w	h
i	o	e	s	b	t	n	g	e	u
r	d	v	e	c	u	n	d	e	r
l	f	e	e	d	r	m	u	d	s
f	d	r	n	f	n	b	i	r	d
i	g	i	r	l	z	o	o	r	a
r	o	p	t	F	r	i	d	a	y
s	e	e	d	i	b	u	r	n	s
t	a	s	u	r	f	o	v	e	r

What am I?

9. (a) I have wings.
   I love to eat seeds.
   I am many colours.

   I am a _____.

   (b) I am many different sizes.
   I am thin.
   You often write on me.

   I am _____.

   (c) I am white and frothy.
   I am on the sea.
   I am made by the waves.

   I am _____.

Syllables

Words can be broken into syllables or word parts. This can help us to spell words. Each syllable has a vowel sound. For example, 'away' has two syllables – 'a' and 'way'.

10. Write how many syllables are in each word.

   (a) paper _____

   (b) Friday _____

   (c) seed _____

   (d) under _____

Unit 17

oa | ow

Look

Say

Trace

Cover

Write

Check

List Words	Practise	Practise	T	D
moan				
coat				
loaf				
float				
soap				
load				
grow				
show				
tow				
below				
own				
crow				
slow				
Saturday				
Sunday				

Picture Matching

1. Write the word that matches each picture.

(a) _____

(b) _____

(c) _____

Missing Letters

2. Write '**oa**' or '**ow**' to complete the words.

(a) gr__ __   (b) c__ __t

(c) l__ __d   (d) bel__ __

(e) fl__ __t   (f) sh__ __

(g) sl__ __   (h) m__ __n

Crossword

3. Use list words to solve the crossword.

Across

1. You wash with it.
2. A black bird.
3. Bread.
4. Day before Monday.
6. To possess.
7. Under.
10. Day after Friday.
11. To pull along.

Down

1. Opposite of 'fast'.
2. You wear it when it's cold.
3. ____ the sand on the truck.
4. He wants to see a ____.
5. To be held up without sinking.
8. To complain.
9. To get bigger.

Word Hunt

4. (a) Which word has the most letters? _____

(b) Which words have the word 'oat' in them?

_____ _____

(c) Which words have the word 'low' in them?

_____ _____

(d) Which words have the fewest letters?

_____ _____

Unit 17

oa ow

List Words

moan
coat
loaf
float
soap
load
grow
show
tow
below
own
crow
slow
Saturday
Sunday

Revision Words

send
bend
band
hand
ball
small

Spelling Rule

Plurals

Words ending in 'f' change 'f' to 'v' and add 'es'.
Look how loaf is made plural (more than one).

loaf → loaves

5. (a) The ☐ is changed to ☐ and ☐ is added.

(b) Write a sentence that contains each word.

loaf _____

loaves _____

Shape Sorter

6. Write a list or revision word that fits in each shape.

(a)

(b)

(c)

(d)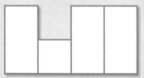

Opposites

7. Find the opposites of these words from the list or revision words.

(a) above _____

(b) big _____

(c) sink _____

(d) fast _____

My gard

Word Search

8. Find the list and revision words in the word search.

moan	load	own	
coat	grow	crow	
loaf	show	slow	
float	tow	Saturday	
soap	below	Sunday	
send	bend	band	
hand	ball	small	

b	e	l	o	w	l	o	a	f	i
a	S	m	a	l	l	w	e	l	l
b	a	n	d	b	e	n	d	o	o
m	t	o	w	m	o	a	n	a	a
S	u	n	d	a	y	c	b	t	d
c	r	o	w	s	l	o	w	b	t
r	d	k	c	s	o	a	p	a	l
h	a	n	d	j	n	t	g	l	h
u	y	s	h	o	w	f	z	l	s
g	r	o	w	d	o	s	e	n	d

Adding Endings

9. Add '**ing**' to these words.

(a) send _____   (b) show _____

(c) moan _____   (d) slow _____

Fill in the Gaps

10. (a) below   (b) float   (c) small

belo___   floa___   smal___

bel___ ___   flo___ ___   sma___ ___

be___ ___ ___   fl___ ___ ___   sm___ ___ ___

b___ ___ ___ ___   f___ ___ ___ ___   s___ ___ ___ ___

___ ___ ___ ___ ___ ___ ___ ___ ___ ___ ___ ___ ___ ___ ___

Unit 18

Summer Holidays

Look

Say

Trace

Cover

Write

Check

List Words	Practise	Practise	T	D
bike				
fish				
shells				
bucket				
spade				
camp				
wave				
tent				
site				
sea				
seagull				
seaweed				
sand				
him				
number				

Word Hunt

1. (a) Which list words begin with the letter 'b'?

_____

_____

(b) Which list word rhymes with 'band'?

_____

(c) Which list word has the letter 'v'?

_____

Shape Sorter

2. Write a word that fits in each shape.

(a)

(b)

(c)

(d)

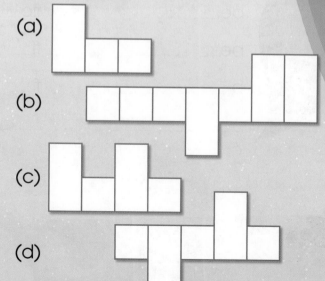

70

My Spelling Workbook B—Prim-Ed Publishing—www.prim-ed.com

Summer Holidays

Crossword

3. Use list words to solve the crossword.

Across

2. You can build a castle with it on the beach.

3.

4.

5.

6.

7.

9. We decided to set up ____ by the lake.

10. Another word for '**ocean**'.

11. A '**6**' or '**7**' or '**9**'.

Down

1.

2. The ____ was perfect for camping.

3.

4.

5.

8. Opposite of '**her**'.

Letters Into Words

4. Write four list words using the letters on the sandcastle.

_____

_____

_____

_____

s d

a i p

e t m c

List Words

bike

fish

shells

bucket

spade

camp

wave

tent

site

sea

seagull

seaweed

sand

him

number

Word Worm

5. Circle each list word you can find in the word worm.

shellsbucketfishbikeseagullspade

All Mixed Up

6. Unjumble these list and revision words.

(a) ties _____

(b) rebmun _____

(c) slehls _____

(d) macp _____

(e) lalb _____

(f) deaps _____

Mixed-up Sentences

7. Unjumble the sentences.

(a) got A dived and to the a sea down fish. seagull

_____

_____

(b) in girl bucket The on. and shells the walked put her

_____

_____

Revision Words

map

car

fun

ball

also

one

Read and Draw

8. (a) A camp site by the sea.

(b) A seagull eating seaweed.

Summer Holidays

Word Search

9. Find the list words in the word search.

bike   fish   shells

bucket   spade   camp

wave   tent   site

sea   seagull   seaweed

sand   him   number

map   car   fun

ball   also   one

```
              x
        s  o
        h  i  m
     e  s  a  h
     l  i  r  p  o
     l  t  x  b  n  s
     s  e  a  w  e  e  d
     j  g  r  u  a  l  s  o
     w  e  s  p  a  d  e  h  w
     a  m  o  e  n  w  t  z  o
     v
```

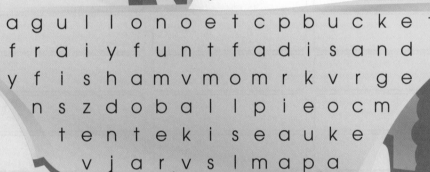

```
s  e  a  g  u  l  l  o  n  o  e  t  c  p  b  u  c  k  e  t  a
c  f  r  a  i  y  f  u  n  t  f  a  d  i  s  a  n  d  i
y  f  i  s  h  a  m  v  m  o  m  r  k  v  r  g  e
n  s  z  d  o  b  a  l  l  p  i  e  o  c  m
t  e  n  t  e  k  i  s  e  a  u  k  e
v  j  a  r  v  s  l  m  a  p  a
```

Missing Letters

10. Write the missing letters.

(a) s__ __w__ __d   (b) __ls__   (c) b__ __k__ __

(d) __u__b__r   (e) f__ __ __ __   (f) sp__d__

Rhyming Words

11. Write list or revision words that rhyme with:

(a) dish   _____

(b) sent   _____

(c) fade   _____

(d) save   _____

(e) hall   _____

Different Meanings

12. The word '**wave**' has more than one meaning. Write two sentences that show each meaning.

(a) _____

_____

(b) _____

_____

Difficult words I Have Found

Word	Practise	Practise	Practise

My Spelling Workbook B—Prim-Ed Publishing—www.prim-ed.com

Aa

Bb

Cc

Dd

Ee

Ff

My Spelling Dictionary: Gg to Ll

Gg

Hh

Ii

Jj

Kk

Ll

Mm

Nn

Oo

Pp

Qq

Rr

Ss

Tt

Uu

Vv

Ww

Xx

Yy

Zz